Before reading this book, the

- two or more letters can repre:
- the spellings <or> <a> <aw> <au> <al> can represent the souna or

This book introduces:
- the spellings <or> <a> <aw> <au> <al> for the sound 'or'
- text at 2 syllable level
  This text has one 3 syllable word: 'awfully'

High-frequency words:
you, are, too, out, he, said, to, was, one, saw, she

Vocabulary:
haunted   – visited by ghosts
dawn   – when it begins to grow light in the morning
chalk   - a white or coloured stick made of a soft rock
                used to write on blackboards
lawn   - an area of mown grass in a garden

Talk about the story

Dan camps in the garden with his
friend. He thinks that his little
sister Viv is too small to camp out.
Find out what happens in the night...

Reading Practice

Practise blending these sounds into words:

a	or	aw
ball	or	saw
call	for	paw
tall	nor	claw
fall	born	lawn
salt	sort	awful
small	form	

al	lord	au
talk	fork	Paul
walk	north	fault
stalk	short	haunt
chalk	sport	August
	storm	Autumn

The Tent on the Lawn

Dan set up a big tent on the lawn. "You are too small to camp out at night," he told Viv.

"But I am awfully brave," said Viv.

"Alright," said Mum, "but don't

talk all night." Viv began to yawn.

"Viv is asleep. Let's tell stories,"

said Liz. "A boy called Paul

lived next to a haunted house."

"One day, he kicked his ball over the wall. When he walked to the house, he saw a ghost."

Dan was afraid of the story.

His face was as white as chalk.

He ran home to his Mum.

The next morning, Viv woke up at dawn. "Dan is not in the tent," she said. "He isn't brave at all!"

Questions for discussion:

- Why did Dan not want Viv to sleep in the tent with his friend?

- Why did Dan run back to the house?

- What do you think Dan said the next morning?

Reading game with the sound 'or'

Play as pelmanism or use for reading practice. Enlarge and photocopy the page twice on two different colours of card. Cut the cards up to play.
Ensure the players sound out the words.

fork	jaw	small
talk	Paul	torn
dawn	fall	walk
fault	short	crawl
salt	chalk	August